INCREDIBLE INSECTS
coloring book

Designs by CHRISTOPHER MARLEY

As a child, artist Christopher Marley was afraid of bugs! But now he travels the world to study them, collect them, and arrange them into dazzling works of art. You'll find twenty-two of his insect images in this coloring book. They are shown as small reproductions on the inside front and back covers. You can have fun creating insect art, too, by copying the colors as arranged by Christopher Marley or by using your own favorite colors. Each drawing is accompanied by a question about the insects—the answers are printed upside down on the back of this page.

The last page of this book is blank so that you can draw and color your own insect picture. Perhaps it will be one you have seen in your neighborhood or in your school yard. Or it may be a fantastic creature that crawls or flies out of your vivid imagination!

Pomegranate Kids™

This coloring book contains images of the following Incredible Insects:

1. Beetles
2. Giant Comet Moth
3. Butterflies known as Whites, Sulphurs, and Jezebels
4. Frog-leg Beetle
5. Asian Flower Beetles
6. Sabertooth Longhorn Beetle
7. Day-flying Moths
8. Rainbow Stag Beetle and Rainbow Tiger Beetle
9. Jewel Beetles
10. Shield Bugs
11. Metallic Wood-boring Beetles
12. Metallic Wasp and Dimpled Longhorn Beetle
13. Beetles
14. Shield Bugs
15. Sunset Moth
16. Ground Beetles
17. Leaf Beetles
18. Lantern Flies
19. Gilded Longhorn Beetles
20. Brushfoot Butterflies
21. Weevils
22. Calodema Wood-boring Beetle

Answers:

1. The little guy in the middle with the polka dots.
2. It is the longest, but two moths have wider wingspans. The atlas moth of Southeast Asia has the second-widest, and the ghost moth of Latin America has the widest wingspan of any butterfly or moth in the world.
3. All are shown upside down.
4. A frog. Frog-leg beetles can't jump at all; they walk just like regular beetles.
5. They are usually found on flowers, eating pollen and nectar.
6. There are two other contenders for "world's largest beetle": the Hercules beetle, and the titan beetle. All three (including the sabertooth longhorn beetle) are found in the Amazon Basin.
7. Sort of—there are about three dozen species in the Hedyliidae family that are considered moth-butterflies, which fly at night. They live in Latin America.
8. The tiger beetle on the right, if it were the size of a human, it could easily run 250 mph!
9. Six: Australia, French Guiana, Indonesia, Madagascar, Malaysia, and Thailand.
10. The aphid.
11. Their larvae love to eat the wood of dying trees.
12. Longhorn beetles have very sharp mandibles, almost like a parrot's beak. The largest species could actually cut off a finger!
13. The blue-and-yellow guy (Thrincopyge alacris), second from the top and second column in from the right, is an American.
14. They can, even though they appear to be flightless. Most flying insects have two hard wing covers that separate in the middle, allowing the flying pair of wings to function. Shield bugs have only one seamless cover that flips up like the trunk of a car to allow the flying set of wings to function. It looks a little strange, but it works!
15. The wings were used in making jewelry.
16. Bombardier beetles can eject small "bombs" of poisonous gas that is strong enough to kill their predators and cause painful burns in humans. Accompanying such ejections is a loud popping sound that completes the illusion of a small explosion.
17. Potatoes.
18. It used to be believed that they could light up the round tips of their heads at night.
19. Most of the 20,000 or more species of longhorn beetles have very long antennae. The antennae of some can be more than twice the length of the body!
20. South America.
21. Five. Many of the tropical weevils have several different color forms even within a single species.
22. It is nearly impossible to reach their territory in remote Papua New Guinea. The few rough roads leading into their habitat are routinely washed out by heavy rains, so the only way to reach their dangerous territory is on foot or by helicopter! Consequently, very few are ever found.

Pomegranate Communications, Inc.
Box 808022, Petaluma CA 94975
800 227 1428
www.pomegranate.com

© 2010 Christopher Marley / Form and Pheromone
www.formandpheromone.com

Catalog No. CB114

Designed and rendered by Oky Sulistio

Printed in Korea, Fall 2009

Pomegranate Europe Ltd.
Unit 1, Heathcote Business Centre, Hurlbutt Road
Warwick, Warwickshire CV34 6TD, UK
[+44] 0 1926 430111
sales@pomeurope.co.uk

This product is in compliance with the Consumer Product Safety Improvement Act of 2008 (CPSIA). A General Conformity Certificate concerning Pomegranate's compliance with the CPSIA is available on our website at www.pomegranate.com, or by request at 800 227 1428.

For additional CPSIA-required tracking details, contact Pomegranate at 800 227 1428.

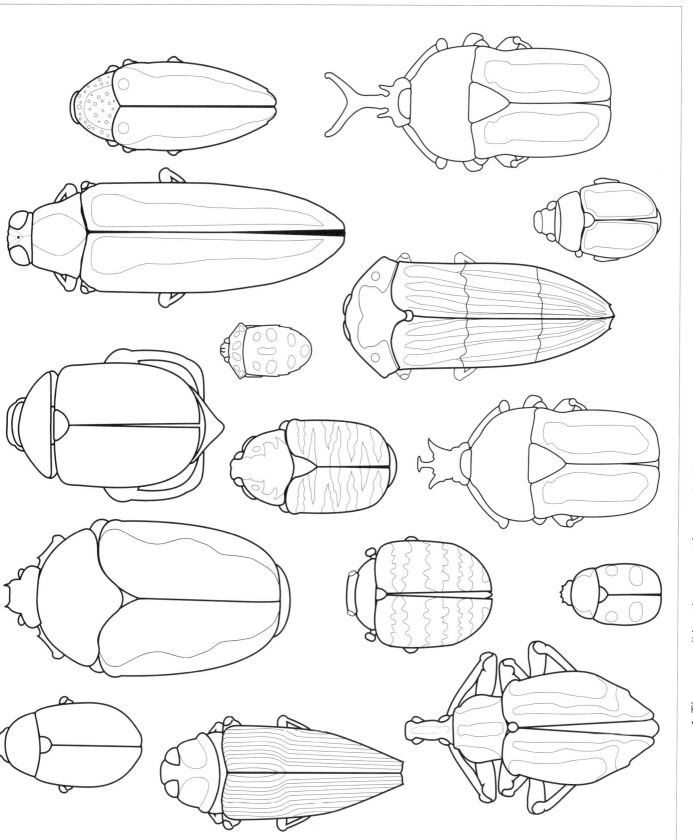

1. These are all beetles except for one that is considered a true bug—can you guess which one it is?

(Hint: True bugs, unlike beetles, have no moving mouth parts and therefore cannot bite or chew. They feed through a stiff "straw" called a proboscis.)

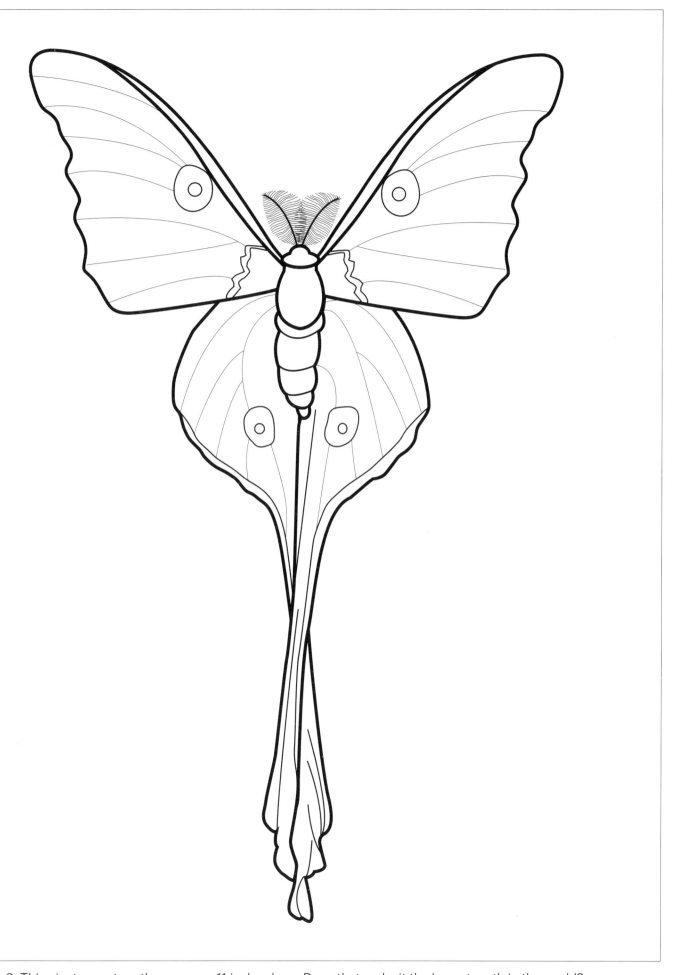

2. This giant comet moth measures 11 inches long. Does that make it the largest moth in the world?

3. Are these butterflies shown right side up or upside down?

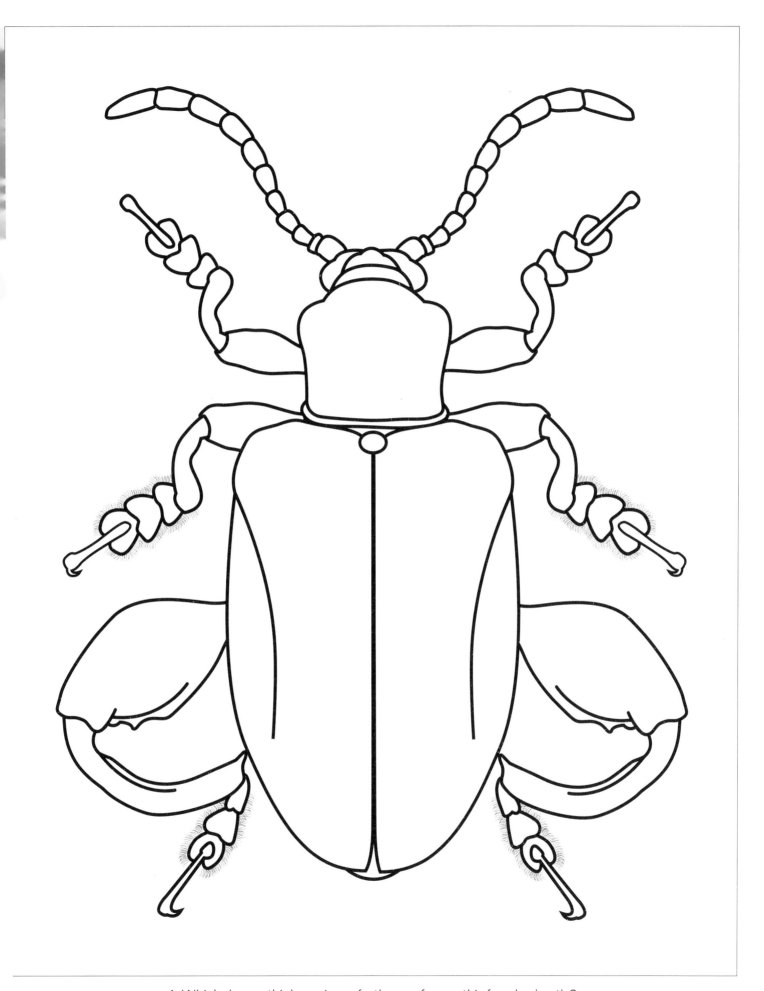

4. Which do you think can jump farther—a frog or this frog-leg beetle?

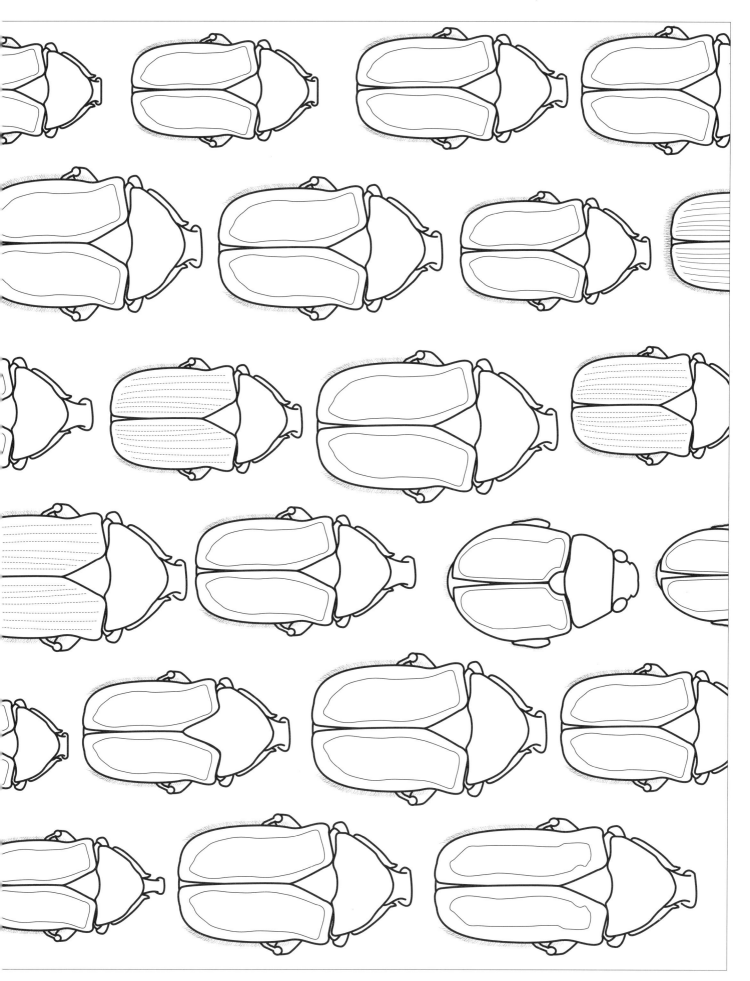

5. Why do you think these flower beetles are called flower beetles?

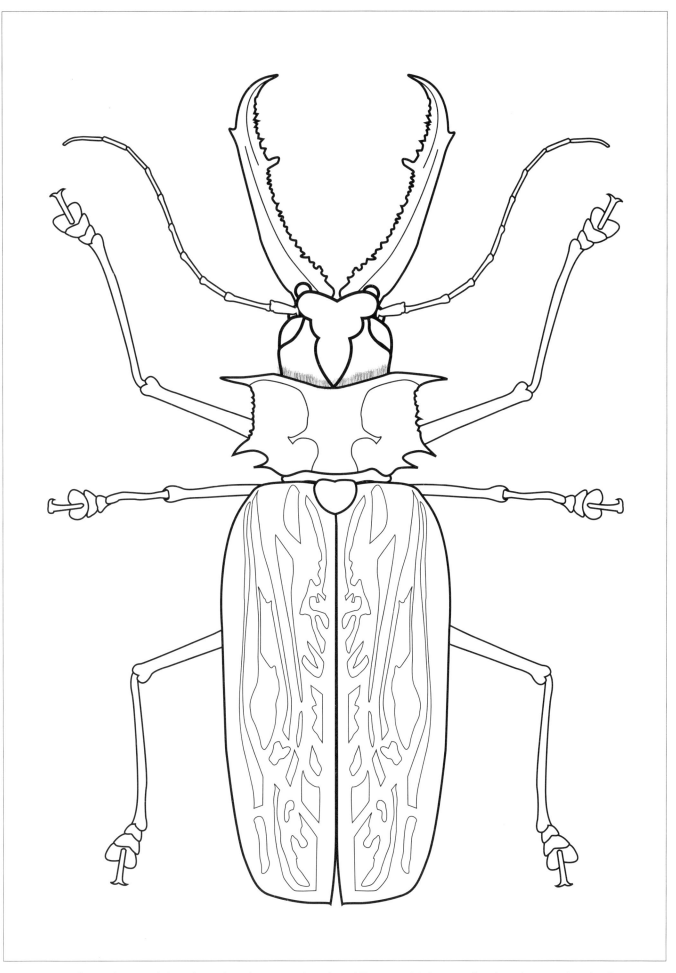

6. This sabertooth longhorn beetle is 7 inches long! Do you think any other beetles get that big?

7. These are day-flying moths. Are there any night-flying butterflies?

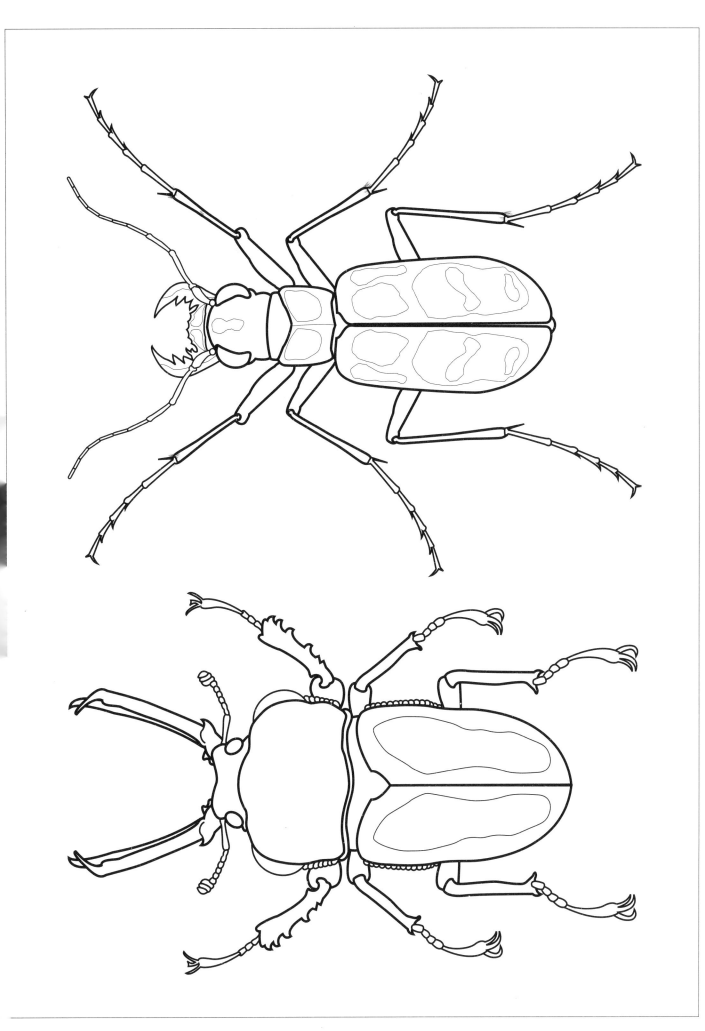

8. One of these beetles is the fastest-running insect in the world: which one?

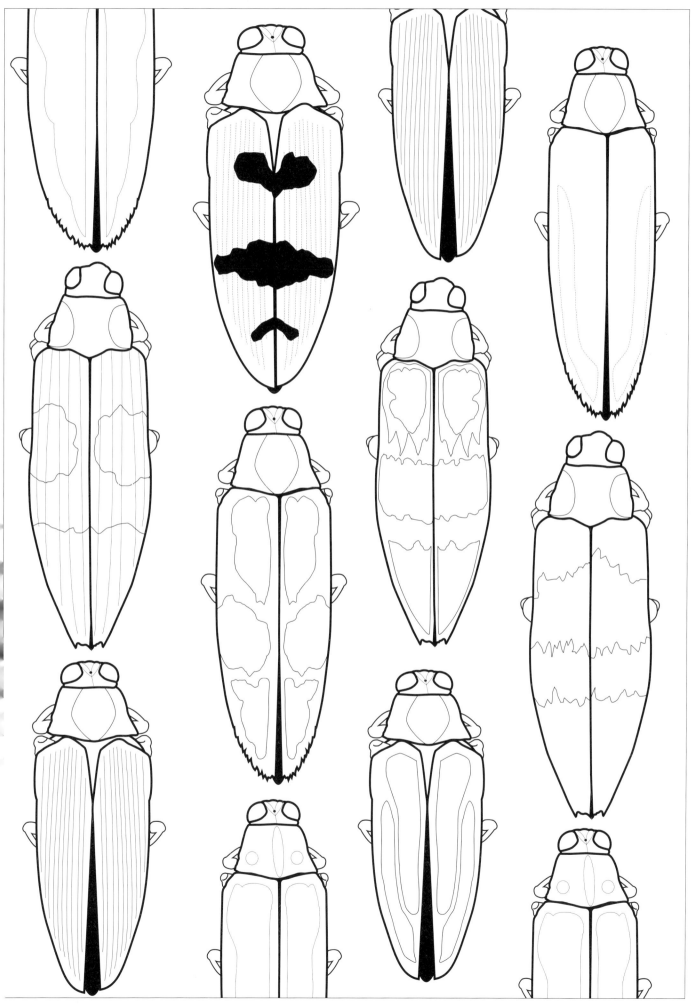

9. How many different countries do the jewel beetles on this page come from?

10. True bugs (insects that feed through a stiff proboscis instead of biting and chewing), like these shield bugs, have one tiny family member that is the most famous crop pest of all. Can you guess what it is?

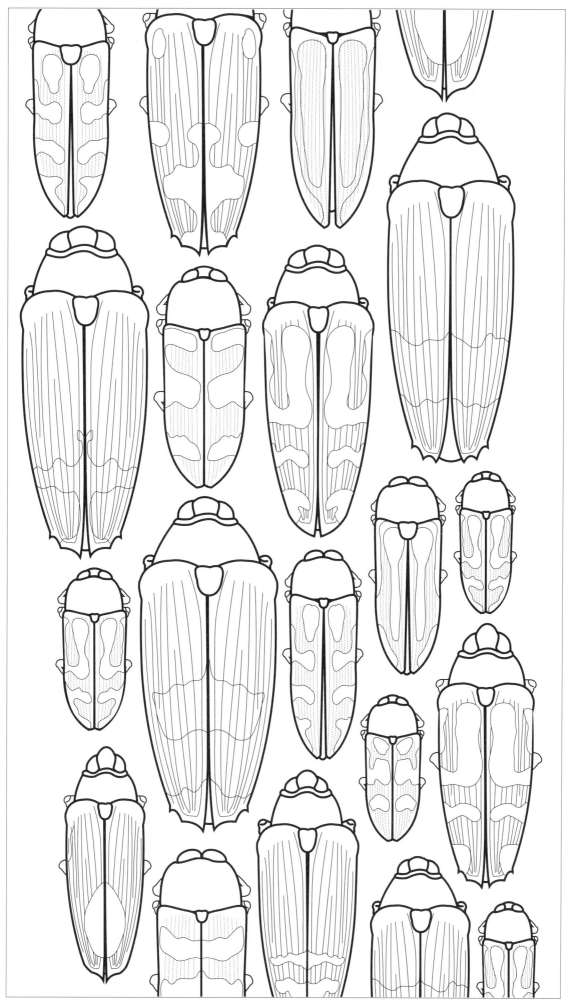

11. Most insects do all they can to escape a forest fire, but many metallic wood-boring beetles are actually attracted to forest fires and can arrive in swarms. Can you guess why?

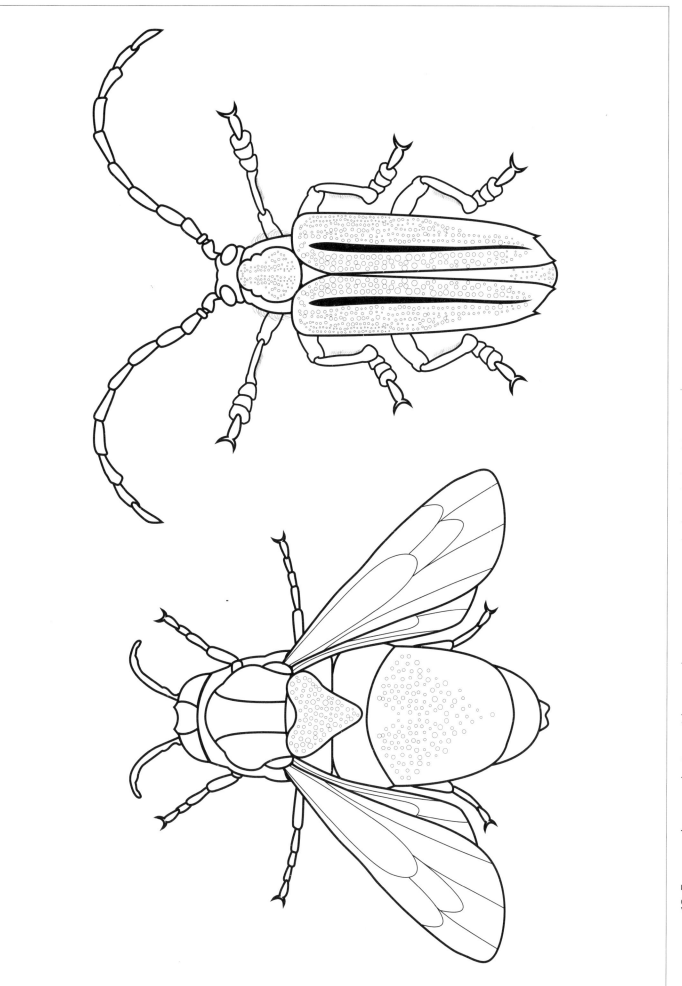

12. Everyone knows why to avoid wasps, but can you guess why knowledgeable insect collectors are very careful with longhorn beetles?

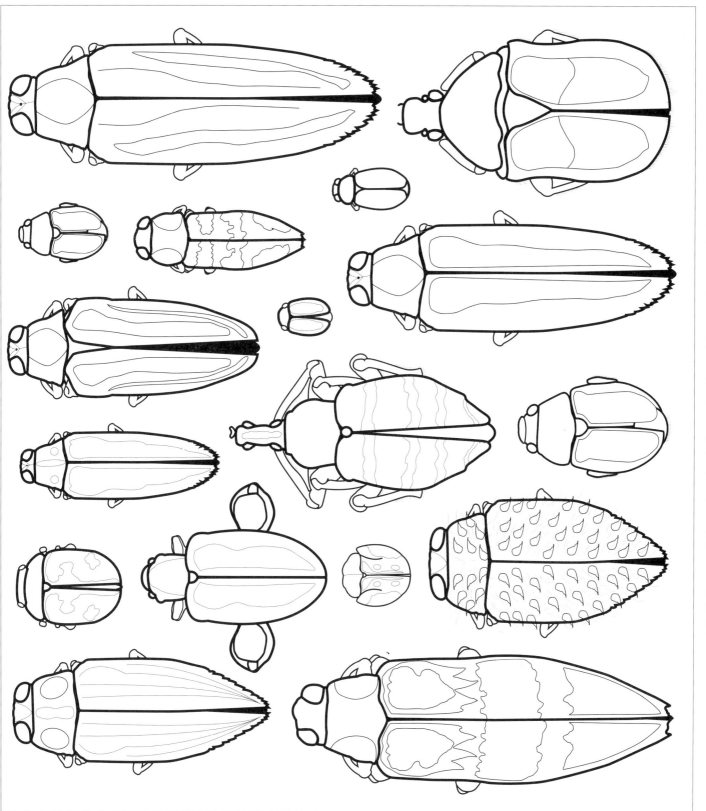

13. Only one of these beetles is from the United States. Guess which one!

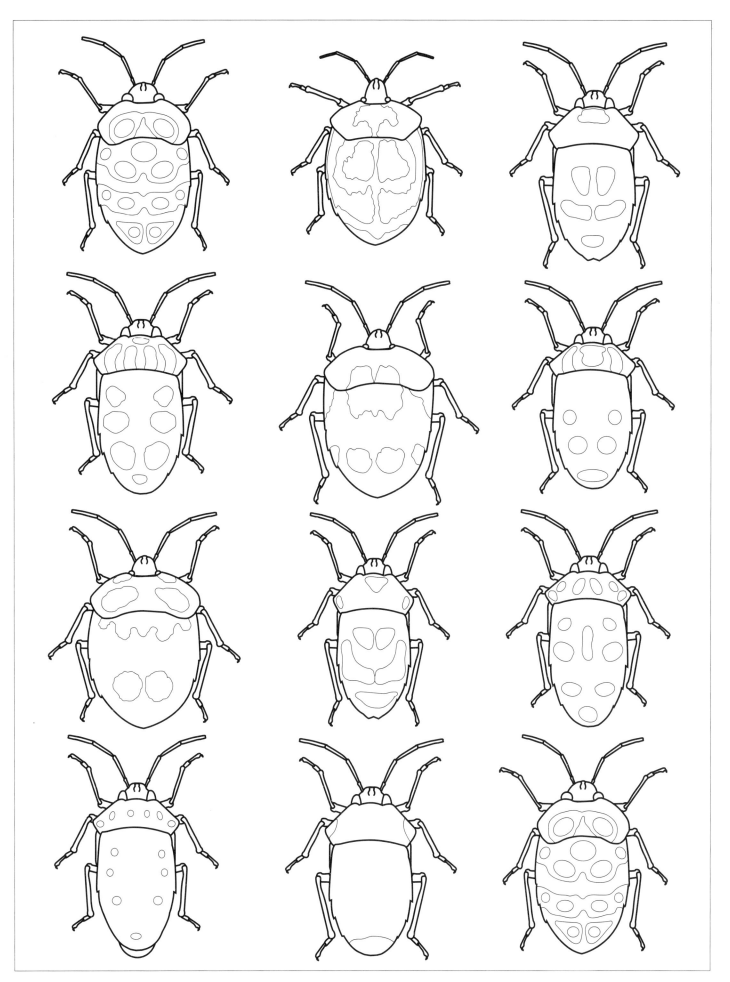

14. Do you think that these shield bugs can fly?

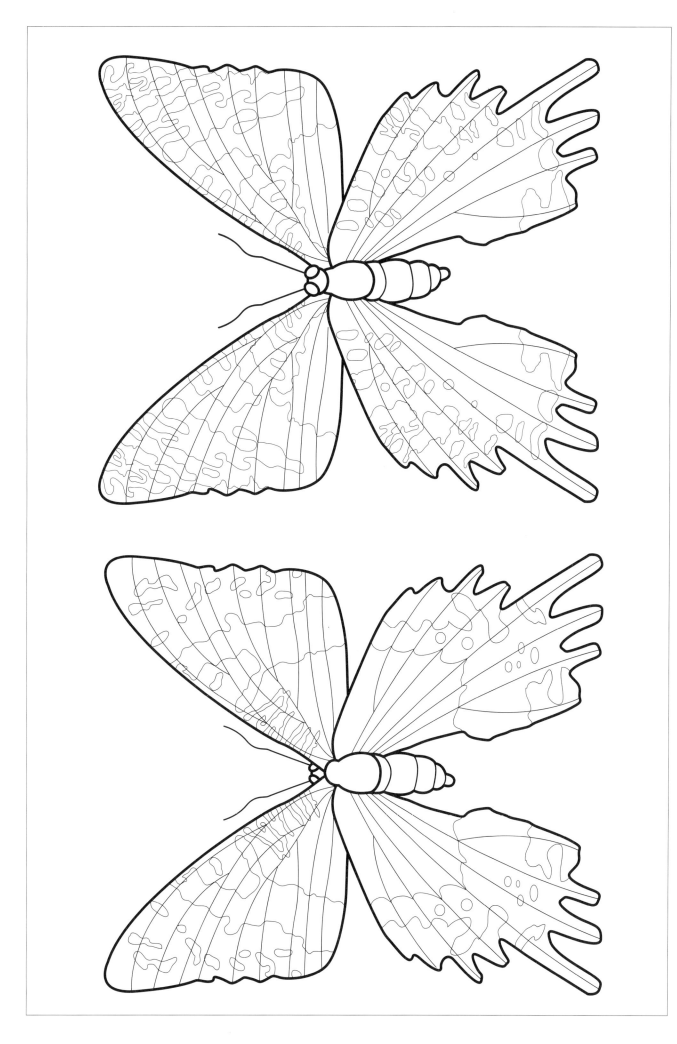

15. This sunset moth was highly prized in Elizabethan England (more than 400 years ago) for an unusual reason. Can you guess what it was?

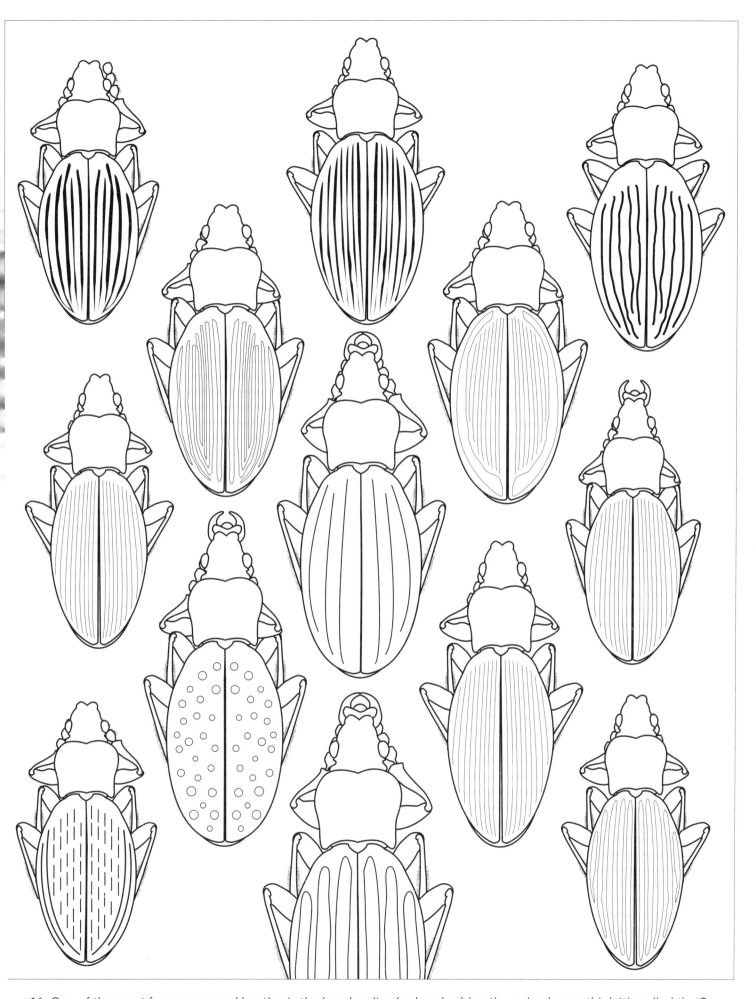

16. One of the most famous ground beetles is the bombardier (or bomber) beetle—why do you think it's called that?

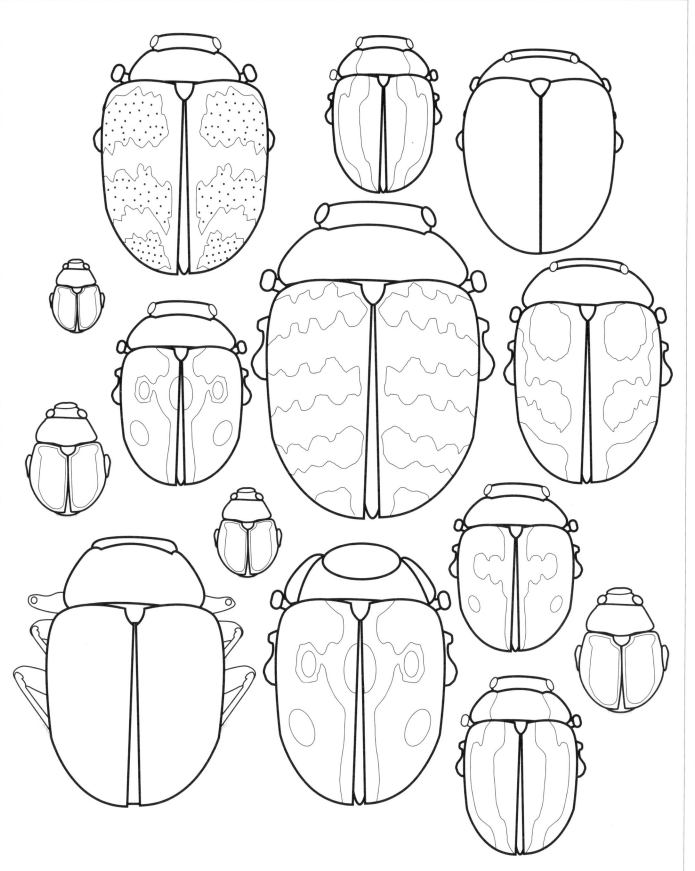

17. Leaf beetles are most famous in the United States and Europe for their ability to destroy entire crops of what vegetable?

18. Can you guess how lantern flies got their name?

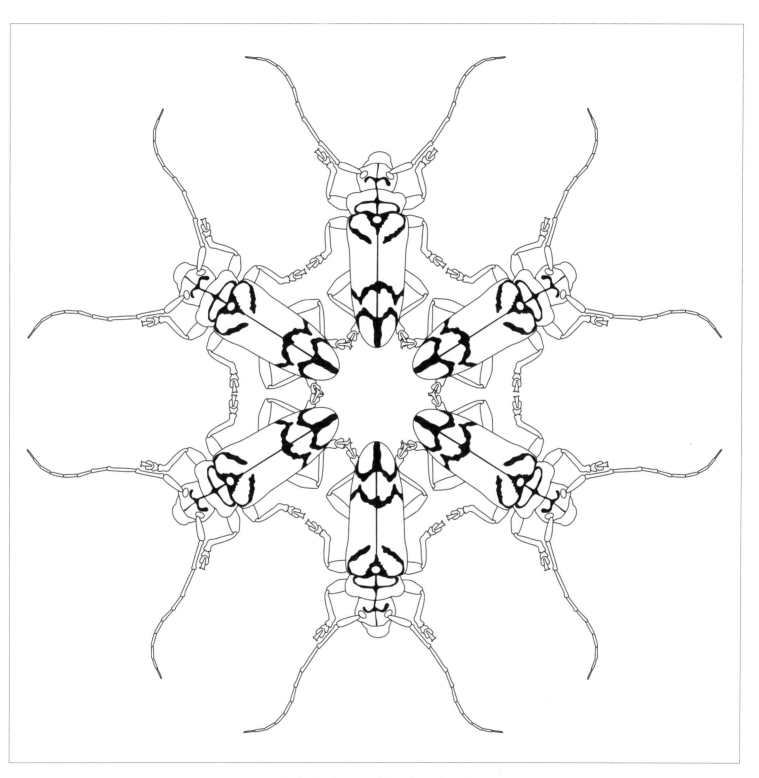

19. How do you think the family of longhorn beetles got its name?

20. All of the world's "88" butterflies come from the same region—can you guess where?

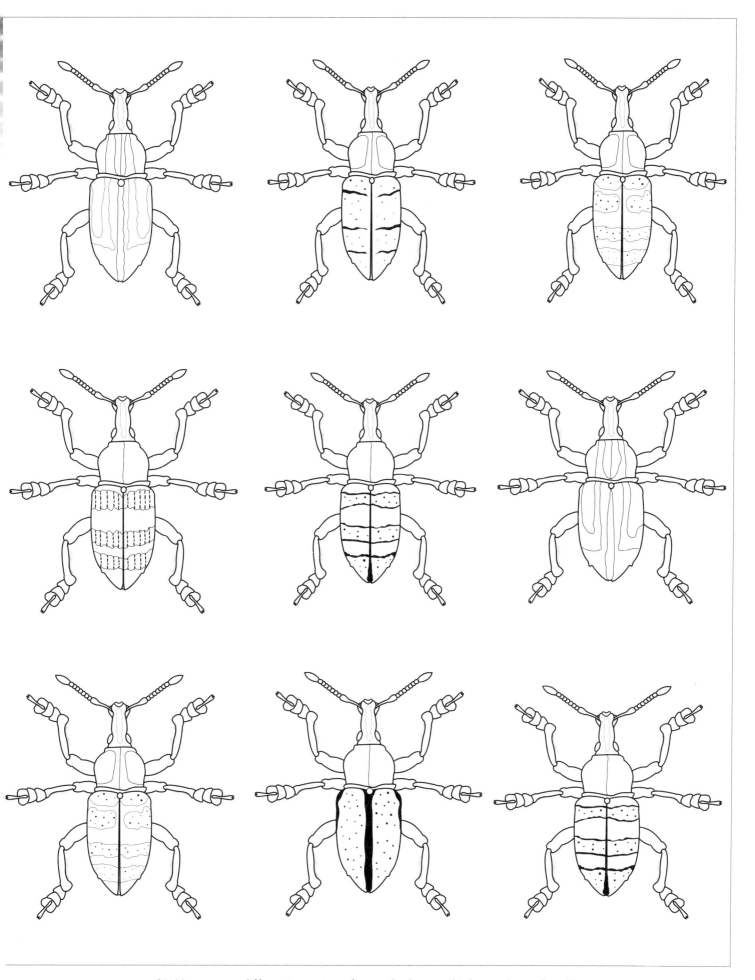

21. How many different species of weevils do you think are shown here?

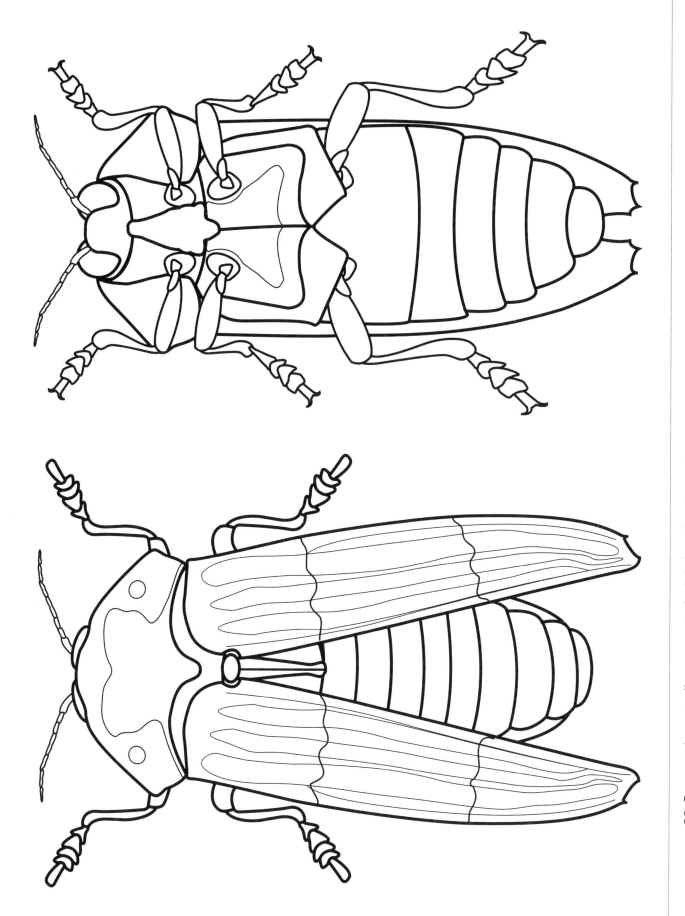

22. For most insect collectors, a single *Calodema* beetle would be the prize of their entire collection. Can you guess why?

Draw and color your own picture here!